Disney · PIXAR

TOY STORY 3

Level 4

Re-told by: Mo Sanders
Series Editor: Rachel Wilson

Pearson Education Limited
KAO Two
KAO Park, Harlow,
Essex, CMI7 9NA, England
and Associated Companies throughout the world.

ISBN: 978-1-2923-4681-6

This edition first published by Pearson Education Ltd 2020

1 3 5 7 9 10 8 6 4 2

Set in Heinemann Roman Special, 14pt/23pt
Printed by Neografia, Slovakia

Published by Pearson Education Limited

Acknowledgments
Shutterstock.com: LesiChkalll27 24, nexus 7 24, Vladimir Gjorgiev 24

For a complete list of the titles available in the Pearson English Readers series, visit
www.pearsonenglishreaders.com.

Alternatively, write to your local Pearson Education office or
to Pearson English Readers Marketing Department,
Pearson Education, KAO Two, KAO Park, Harlow, Essex, CMI7 9NA

In This Book

Woody
A sheriff and Andy's favorite toy in the past

Buzz Lightyear
A space ranger toy and Woody's best friend

Jessie
A cowgirl who is Andy's toy

Lotso
A toy bear at the daycare center

Big Baby
A baby doll who always listens to Lotso

Bonnie
A little girl who goes to Sunnyside Daycare Center

Before You Read

Introduction

Andy is going to leave for college and his mom makes a terrible mistake. She doesn't put his old toys in the attic; she takes them to a daycare center for little children. Can Woody save his friends from this terrible place? Can the toys come home?

Activities

1 **Look at the pictures on each page. Choose the correct answers.**

1 Where are the toys? (page 1)
  a in the attic   **b** in a daycare center   **c** in Andy's room
2 Where are the toys? (page 7)
  a in a toy store   **b** in a daycare center   **c** in a house
3 What is Woody doing? (page 12)
  a leaving the daycare center   **b** coming to help his friends
  c hiding in a bag

2 **Look at the two pictures on page 1 and discuss what is different.**

1 How old is Andy?
2 Does he like playing with toys?

Years ago, Andy played with his toys every day. His favorite
toys were Woody the sheriff and Buzz the space ranger.
But now Andy was older. It was time for college.
Andy put all his toys in a big, black bag. After he left,
they could go in the attic. Andy only wanted to bring
Woody with him to college.

Later, Andy's mom saw the bag outside Andy's room.
She thought it was trash, but really it was Andy's toys. She took
the bag outside. Woody watched her from the door of Andy's
room.

"Oh, no!" he said. "Andy's mom is making a mistake. That bag
is for the attic. It isn't trash! I must save my friends!"

The toys got out of the trash bag and into a box with
SUNNYSIDE on it.

"Jump out!" Woody cried.

"Perhaps the Sunnyside Daycare Center is better for us,"
said Jessie.

"No! Andy's mom made a mistake!" cried Woody.

Suddenly, Andy's mom shut the car door. But Woody was in the
car, too! She drove to Sunnyside Daycare Center.

At the daycare center, a teacher took the box of toys to one
of the classrooms. There were a lot of toys there.

"Welcome to Sunnyside!" said a pink bear. His name was Lotso.

Andy's toys liked this place.

"We can have a new life here," Jessie said.

"Let's stay!" cried Slinky Dog.

But Woody wasn't happy.

"We're Andy's toys," Woody said. "We must go home!"
He was angry because his friends didn't follow him to the door.
Woody ran out of the classroom. What was the best way for
him to leave? He climbed through a window and up to the
roof. He couldn't jump from there, but then he saw a kite.

"I can fly!" said Woody.

He held the kite and jumped. The kite flew up over
Sunnyside's walls. But suddenly the kite fell down into a tree.
Now Woody couldn't move. A little girl from the daycare center
saw him in the tree. Her name was Bonnie. Bonnie took Woody
and put him in her bag.

At Sunnyside, Andy's toys were excited about their new life.
But then the children ran into the classroom. These children
were very young. They didn't know how to play with the toys.
They dropped them and threw them. They hit them and hurt
them. They painted with them. They tried to eat them!
"This is terrible!" said Buzz.

That night, Buzz climbed out of the classroom.

"Lotso's nice. He can help us," Buzz told the other toys.

But Lotso wasn't nice now. "You can stay with us in our nice classroom," he told Buzz. "But your friends must stay with the little children!"

"No!" cried Buzz.

Lotso told the Sunnyside toys to push Buzz to the floor.

"Move the switch on his back," Lotso said.

After the toys moved the switch, Buzz couldn't remember his name or his friends. Lotso took Buzz back to his old classroom.

"We're leaving," said Jessie.

"No!" said Lotso.

"Who's going to stop us?" asked Jessie.

Suddenly, Buzz jumped out! He only listened to Lotso now. He stopped his old friends easily.

"Now put them all in prison!" Lotso said.

Buzz and the Sunnyside toys put Andy's toys in toy baskets.

"Buzz!" cried Jessie. "We're your friends!"

But Buzz didn't remember her now.

"You new toys must learn about life at Sunnyside," Lotso said.

"Now sleep well, because tomorrow the little children are
going to play with you again!"

Woody was at Bonnie's house, but he wanted to go home.
"Are your friends there?" asked a toy.
"They're at Sunnyside," Woody said.
"Sunnyside!" Bonnie's toys knew all about Lotso. A long time
ago, Lotso and Big Baby were the toys of a girl called Daisy.
But Daisy lost them and Lotso became sad and angry. Woody
knew then—he *had* to help his friends.

The next morning, Woody hid inside Bonnie's bag. At Sunnyside, he climbed out and ran back to the old classroom. He watched the little children playing. Bonnie's toys were right—this *was* a terrible place. After the children left, Woody ran to his friends.

"Woody!" they cried happily.

Woody smiled. "We're going to leave *tonight*," he said.

Before the toys could leave, there was a problem—Buzz.
But Woody had a plan.

"Now!" he shouted. The toys jumped on Buzz. They moved
the switch on the space ranger's back. Buzz looked up.

"What's happening?" he asked.

"You came back!" cried Jessie.

"Yes," said Buzz. "Where was I?"

The toys ran outside into the yard of the daycare center.
It was very dark.
Woody pointed to a trash chute in one of the walls. "That's the
only way out," he said.
The toys started to move carefully across the yard. They didn't
want any of Lotso's toys to hear them. Soon they were at
the chute.

The toys were afraid because the chute was dark. What was at the bottom?

"Come on!" said Woody, and he jumped.

The toys followed him. There was a dumpster at the bottom.

"We have to go across it," cried Woody.

But suddenly, Lotso was there. The Sunnyside toys were with him.

"Where are you all going?" the bear asked angrily.

"We're going home to Andy," said Woody.
"Andy doesn't love you!" cried Lotso. "Children don't *really*
love their toys!"

"*Daisy* loved you, Lotso!' said Woody. "She didn't mean
to lose you."
"She left me!" shouted Lotso. "So we left *her*!"
Big Baby was angry now. He remembered Daisy. He took Lotso
in his arms and threw him into the dumpster!

Woody, Buzz, and their friends ran for hours and hours. They arrived at Andy's house early in the morning. The toys jumped into a box with the word ATTIC on it. Only Woody stayed on the floor.

"Goodbye, Woody!" said all the toys. "Have a good time at college with Andy!"

Woody climbed into a box with COLLEGE on it.

Andy and his mom came into the room. His mom started to cry.

"It's okay," Andy said. "I'm going to love college!"

Inside the box, Woody had an idea.

After Andy and his mom left, Woody jumped out. He wrote a new name and address on the box with ATTIC on it.

Andy came back and read the address on the box.
He drove to the address on the box. It was Bonnie's house.
Andy showed the toys to Bonnie.
"These were my toys," he told her. "I want you to have
them now."

Andy and Bonnie played with the toys.

Then Andy stood up. He had to drive to college.

Woody looked at Andy and remembered all the good times.

"Now we're going to have good times with Bonnie," said Buzz
to his old friend.

It was true. This was the start of a happy new life for the toys.

After You Read

1 **Read and say True or False.**

1 Andy wanted to give his old toys to the daycare center.

2 Mom made a mistake with the bag of toys.

3 All Woody's friends wanted to stay at the Sunnyside Daycare Center.

4 Woody left the daycare center by kite.

5 Woody went from the daycare center to Andy's house.

2 **Put the story into the correct order.**

a Buzz couldn't remember his friends.

b Woody climbed up to the roof of the daycare center.

c Andy gave his toys to Bonnie.

d Bonnie took Woody to her house.

e Mom took Andy's toys to the daycare center.

f Woody came back to the center for his friends.

g Big Baby threw Lotso in the dumpster.

3 **Who is your favorite toy in the story? Why?**
Discuss with a friend.

Glossary

attic (*noun*) a small room below the roof of a house

basket (*noun*) a thing you can use to put or carry your toys in

box (*noun*) a thing you use to keep things in. It usually has a top

chute (*noun*) a thing you drop trash into to throw it away

classroom (*noun*) a room in a school where children have lessons

college (*noun*) a place young men and women go to study

cowgirl (*noun*) a woman who rides a horse and works with cows

daycare center (*noun*) a place parents can leave young children and babies during the day

dumpster (*noun*) a large box that trash goes in

kite (*noun*) a toy that you can fly in the air

prison (*noun*) a place people go after they do a bad thing

roof (*noun*) the top part of a house, on the outside

sheriff (*noun*) a kind of police officer in the USA

space ranger (*noun*) a kind of police officer in stories about space

switch (*noun*) you can stop or start a thing—a light or a toy—by moving this up or down

trash (*noun*) a thing people throw away because they do not want it

Phonics

Say the sounds. Read the words.

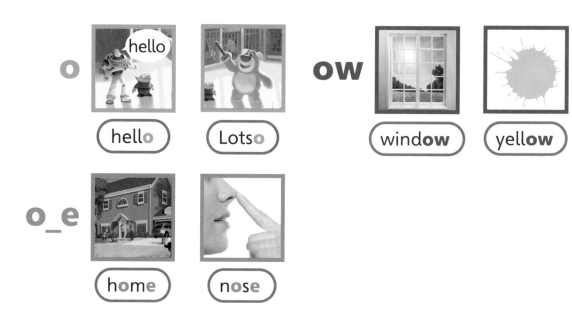

o

hello

Lotso

ow

window

yellow

o_e

home

nose

Say the rhyme.

Mom drove us here in a box in her car,
To Sunnyside Center. It wasn't so hard.

Lotso the bear said hello to us first.
We didn't know it then but Lotso's the worst!

Only Woody knew, and he wanted to go,
So he jumped through the window to the yard below.

Values

Change can be good.

Goodbye, old friend.

How are you feeling?

I'm feeling sad. How about you?

You're right. And we're Bonnie's toys now. It's going to be fantastic!

I'm sad. But Andy has to go to college. And he's going to have a great time.

Yes, it's going to be *fantastic*!

How did the filmmakers make the Toy Story movies?

There are four *Toy Story* movies in all. The first movie was in 1995 and the last one was in 2019—that's 24 years! Now, Woody, Buzz Lightyear, and all the *Toy Story* characters are famous around the world.

For each movie, the filmmakers drew about 40,000 sketches. These sketches told the story in pictures.

sketches of Bo Peep, a *Toy Story* character

Then, the filmmakers used computers to make the movie. In 1995, this was the first time to make a movie in this way. It was slow work. There was a computer model for every character in the movie. The filmmakers could move the bodies and faces of every character in a thousand different ways.

computer model of Bo Peep